THE MOON
OF THE
MOUNTAIN LIONS

THE MOON
OF THE
MOUNTAIN LIONS

BY JEAN CRAIGHEAD GEORGE
Illustrated by Winifred Lubell

THOMAS Y. CROWELL COMPANY   *New York*

THE SUMMER OF THE FALCON
GULL NUMBER 737
SPRING COMES TO THE OCEAN
HOLD ZERO!
COYOTE IN MANHATTAN
THE MOON OF THE OWLS
THE MOON OF THE BEARS
THE MOON OF THE SALAMANDERS
THE MOON OF THE CHICKAREES
THE MOON OF THE FOX PUPS
THE MOON OF THE MONARCH BUTTERFLIES
THE MOON OF THE WILD PIGS
THE MOON OF THE MOUNTAIN LIONS

The young mountain lion opened his mouth and rolled out his tongue in a waking yawn. Lying in his den at timberline, he turned his gaze upon his kingdom on the side of Mount Olympus in Washington. Snowcapped peaks speared the darkness above him. An alpine meadow splattered with flowers lay downhill to his right, and far down-mountain from him cedar trees hugged the hills and glacial valleys. Below the cedars the rain forest reached to the Pacific Ocean. Stretching, listening, the noble cat arose and quietly stepped into the moonlight.

The young lion was abroad. The animals of the mountainside trembled and lay still.

The quarter moon hung in the August sky, its mellow light falling upon a world making the first, almost unnoticeable, shift to winter. Change was the stuff of this moon: birds turned and flew south, mammals left the meadows to sleep.

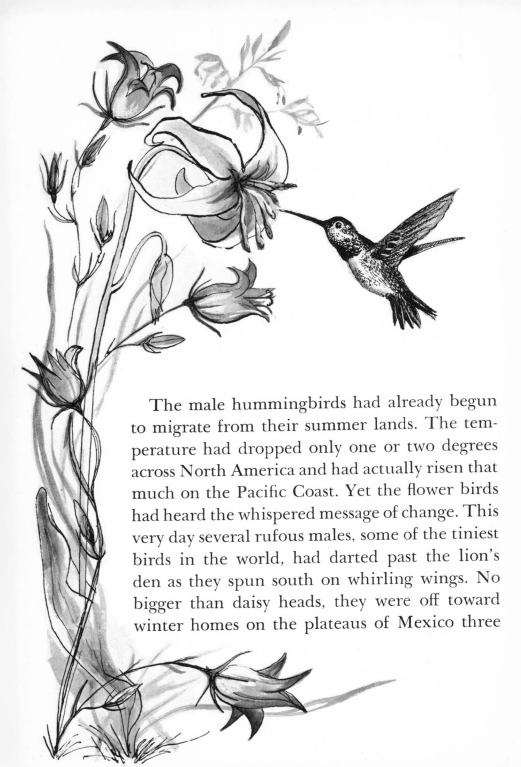

The male hummingbirds had already begun to migrate from their summer lands. The temperature had dropped only one or two degrees across North America and had actually risen that much on the Pacific Coast. Yet the flower birds had heard the whispered message of change. This very day several rufous males, some of the tiniest birds in the world, had darted past the lion's den as they spun south on whirling wings. No bigger than daisy heads, they were off toward winter homes on the plateaus of Mexico three

thousand miles away. Their females hastened the feeding of the young. They would soon see their dime-sized youngsters out of the nest, lead them to the nectar of the last lilies and bellflowers, then follow their males to the winter sun lands.

The swallows also felt the change of the August moon. Great flocks of them were gathering by the thousands and tens of thousands over lakes, marshes, and coasts. Almost always on the wing, these agile birds have tiny, feeble feet that they rarely use. Before the moon waned they would climb the sky higher and higher, higher and higher, until far out of sight of man and beast, they would turn south and speed away. At dawn the swallows would be gone, leaving the skies strangely empty, like beaches when September comes.

3

Other animals were responding differently to the change. In the East and Midwest the chipmunks, toads, and frogs were asleep. This was not the sleep of hibernation, but of estivation — summer's torpor. In this quiet state they were avoiding the adversities of August — dryness and heat.

One beast, however, would combine the sleeps of summer and winter. In the alpine meadow below the lion the whistling marmots were ready for the longest sleep of all the mammals — from mid-August to mid-May, nine months. Some of the marmots were already taking naps that lasted a day or two. Fat and drowsy, they slept longer and longer each time. Eventually they would not be able to awaken until spring. Those that were still up and about whistled like birds in the flower-filled meadows. When the lion came out of his den, however, they were all in their labyrinths and chambers beneath the ground, for they sleep by night.

The lion tasted the wind as it shot up the side of the mountain. The change of aging and ripening was upon the air. Winds smelled of sweet huckleberries. Ripe gooseberries and twinberries perfumed the breezes.

Having looked and scented, the young lion now listened. He harkened intently. The elk and deer had changed their direction. They were no longer climbing among the peaks but moving downward. He heard them snapping branches far below.

Since spring they had been wandering upward toward the alpine meadows as the melting snow uncovered sweet grasses. Now the grasses were dying, the season of the high country was ending, and like the birds, the deer and elk were on migration. Theirs, however, was not south but down the mountain, and this concerned the lion. The deer and elk were his staff of life. He had moved up the mountain with them in the spring, harvesting the weak and infirm as he went. At five thousand feet above sea level, where the trees stopped and the rocks, ice, and alpine prairies took over, the young lion had denned for the summer. His shelter was a twisted thicket of alpine firs, the last trees to withstand the driving wind and stunting cold at the tops of the mountains. They marked the timberline.

Tonight the elk and deer were two thousand feet below the lion in a lower, different kind of forest. This he knew because he could smell the pungent cedar they had tramped and broken. There are no cedars on the mountain above three thousand feet. Only the valiant alpine firs could live at such an elevation. The lion had to go down.

7

Once more he listened. Something stirred in the forest not far below him, and he recognized the limping elk who had injured his foot in a crag. The elk could not travel as fast as the others in his herd. He must be harvested.

The lion stepped gracefully down the rocks, then breaking into bounds, he swung out across the meadow. Beneath his feet a final change was taking place — summer was ending, the next spring beginning. Under the leaf stems of the tiny alpine willow trees, no taller than a thumb, new buds were forming. This was happening not only on the mountain but everywhere across the nation. Next year's elm, maple, beech, and apple buds were being shaped. As these formed, the cells that brought food and water to the leaves began to close off. When all were sealed, the leaves would lose their chlorophyll, turn yellow, and tumble to the ground.

The young lion stopped at the edge of the meadow and listened for the limping elk. Lean and muscular, the lion was magnificently beautiful. Tawny in color, he had black smudges under his eyes and along his nose. His back was as straight as a leveling rod, his paws immense. His tail, tipped with black and almost as long as he, touched the ground and curled up. He weighed more than two hundred pounds. The cougar, or mountain lion, of North America is almost as large as the African lion and is the second largest cat in the New World. Only the jaguar surpasses him in length and weight.

A hundred years ago the mountain lion was abundant in all the mountains of the United States and Canada, both east and west. Now he is rare and is found only in the lonely wilderness areas of the West and in Florida and Louisiana.

9

Washington's Olympic Peninsula, a land barely touched by man, still has its appropriate number of mountain lions. Elk and deer do not become so numerous that they ravage trees and grasses. These herds need no management, for the mountain lion keeps their numbers balanced.

The young lion scanned the deep mountain valley where the Hoh River flowed. He saw the sharp V cut made by the glacier, and far below, the flatlands where the mountain stopped. Then he saw the gleaming surface of the Pacific Ocean stretching into the mist beyond. With a leisurely twist the lion looked up the mountain. The snow-covered peaks of the jagged Olympic Range shone white against the purple-black sky. In the moonlight the glaciers lay like sleeping beasts in the black rocks. He could hear the largest one, Blue Glacier, moan as its tons of ice moved over boulders. Melting now in the August heat, the glacier became water that broke into a waterfall, a stream, and a river, which joined the sea. The lion looked at the ribbon of water that wound below him, then walked onward and downward.

Born three years ago by the August moon —
lion cubs arrive in spring and into summer —
the young lion had lived with his mother and
two sisters in the Enchanted Valley to the south.
He rarely saw his father; his mother had chased
him away when she was ready to give birth. She
would seek him again in two years when her cubs
left her, for lions are faithful to one mate.

After a three-month pregnancy the lioness had
given birth to the twelve-inch-long furry kittens.
In ten days their eyes opened.

They were weaned in three months. By then
the young lion had shed the spots and ringed tail
of his childhood. He weighed about forty
pounds. At this time he ventured forth from the
rock den with his mother and sisters. They trav-
eled far each night to hunt their vast kingdom
of several square miles in the Enchanted Valley.
With their mother they caught grouse, marmots,
coyotes, and — when the cubs were big — deer
and elk. Each dawn they returned to their den.

Often they rolled and played like house cats,
batting stones and flowers around, jumping on
each other. Like house cats they also made many
sounds, each expressing different feelings.

Last July the young lion had left home. He climbed out of the valley, leaped up rocks, and wandered through tall forests as he swung northward. Finally he came to Blue Glacier on Mount Olympus. In the meadow tundra, deer and elk were grazing. No lions challenged him, so he stayed nearby until the moon of change drove the animals down-mountain. Then, taking the same route he was again following this night, he descended to the valley floor, where the stately rain forests lay. Here the elk and deer wintered, and the land was kept forever green by warm rains from the sea. The young lion stayed the winter here.

One night he had stopped to look around him, just as he stopped tonight. Suddenly he had heard a female mountain lion calling from the other side of the Hoh River. Her scream was the high-pitched caterwaul that the young lion recognized as a mother cat's danger call to her kittens. He watched the forest below, purring to the family that occupied the land beyond the river. His whiskers stood out straight and his tail swished emotionally.

Presently the thin cry of a frightened kitten
sounded in the riverbed. Time passed. The
young lion did not move. A stick snapped not
far away. Glancing in the direction of the sound,
he saw the lioness and two cubs slip out of the
alder forest and move up the dry edge of the
river. One kitten was a male; the other was a
female — a lively, beautiful cub who piqued the
interest of the young lion.

The three moved in unison until they came
to a log. The kittens sat down. The mother lay
on her side, and reaching under the fallen tree
with her strong paws, pulled out some game she

15

had cached there. The family set upon it with loud purrs. When the kittens' stomachs were round with good food, the female shoved the leftovers under the log, and kicking leaves over it, led her spotted babies back into the mottled forest. The young lion watched them until they disappeared.

After that he was constantly on the alert for the family. Once or twice he heard the lioness call. He never answered, but stayed cautiously on his side of the river.

He often saw the family and watched them quietly. The kittens grew. Eventually their tumbles and rollicks became skilled pounces and jumps. Then, one spring night, he heard the lioness call from far, far up on the northern end of her kingdom, and the young lion saw and heard no more from the family. He became busy with his own affairs. He followed the elk and deer up the mountains.

Now it was the moon of change again. The young lion was three years old. He was strong and sleek as he walked the night, listening for the limping elk. An hour passed. He heard nothing. Then a rock slipped, off to his left. Once more the "da thump" of the buck echoed through the night. Dropping from a cliff like plunging water, the lion sped across a meadow to the edge of a small lake. Around it sparkled bright alpine flowers: bluebells, yarrow, glacier lilies, cinquefoil, and cow parsnips. They were all blooming at once in the high country, although in the lowlands some were spring flowers and some bloomed in autumn. On the mountain peaks the growing season is so short that everything must rush into blossom between June and September. Spring's bluebells overlap autumn's asters.

As the lion walked beside the lake, he awakened a junco sleeping behind a curtain of moss along the bank. The bird saw the lion-shadow and called the "tik-tik" danger signal of the junco. Her five youngsters, sleeping under roots and flowers nearby, awakened but did not move, for their mother's note was a warning. They tightened their feet on their perches and sat more still.

The youngsters had been flying for only three days. Nevertheless, they knew where the seeds of the alpine flowers lay, and only today they had learned to shell them. Tomorrow they would bathe and the next day they would sun themselves. Then they would move down-mountain with the elk, the deer, and the lion. They would not spend the winter with them, however. In October the juncos would migrate to the middle of the nation. Here they would be known affectionately as "snowbirds," as their white tail feathers flicked brightly over cold gray fields.

The mother junco watched the cascade of starlike avalanche lilies above her head. When they became still she knew the lion had passed. Softly she called the "all's well" signal to her family.

The young lion walked on. The lake broke
into a stream, and the stream into waterfalls. He
felt spray on his nose as he followed the water-
way down the mountain. At three thousand feet
he entered a new kind of forest. The twisted,
wind-torn alpine firs of the high country were
replaced by mountain hemlocks, silver and
Alaska firs, and the cedars he had smelled earlier.
Pinedrops and twinberries grew under the trees.
Different flowers, as well as trees, grow at different elevations on the mountain.

The young lion passed the last home of the whistling marmots. They live high up in the mountains in the zone of the alpine firs and avalanche lilies. Only one mammal lives above them. On the peaks among the crags, the mountain goats — the animals of the top of the world — find food and shelter during the summer. They stay above the trees until the snow falls, and then they descend only as low as the cedar trees. The elk and deer go lower.

On quiet feet the lion hurried onward. The limping elk knew by now that he was being followed. He headed for a rocky slope where he could hide.

The lion saw where the elk was going. He went up-mountain. High above his prey, the lion turned and came straight down upon him, driving him toward a gorge and a waterfall.

Another kind of bird heard the elk pass. A dipper, or water ouzel, peered out from behind a waterfall and shifted his weight from one foot to the other. This amazing bird of the high country was sleeping in an air pocket behind the cascade. He had flown through falling water to this spot. Hopping to a crack in the rock wall, he settled down for the night. He was dry and well hidden. Carefully preening his feathers until they lay so smoothly no water could seep in, he fell asleep.

The bird had been raised in a round nest of moss on the wall beside the cascade. He had stayed in the nest for three weeks — a long time, for songbirds — but each day was important to him. When he finally flew, he had to cross the roaring waterfall to reach land. His wings had to be strong and fully developed to achieve this. He had made the perilous flight two weeks ago.

After alighting he had followed his parents onto the water. Floating like ducks, the tiny songbirds taught him how to ride the swift currents. Eventually the parents maneuvered him to a still pool, where they dove into the crystal water. The young bird followed them, watching silver bubbles pass his eyes as he pumped to the bottom. Rolling, darting, the three birds swam among the stones, hunting the larvae of the black fly. Surfacing, they flew out of the water, and judging the force of the cascade, winged behind it. In glassy air pockets they rested, safe from hawk, bass, and weasel.

Now the young dipper was independent of his parents. He slept alone behind the cascade. The lion approached, but the bird did not stir. Not even a mountain lion would try to walk into such a deathtrap as the thunderous waterfall.

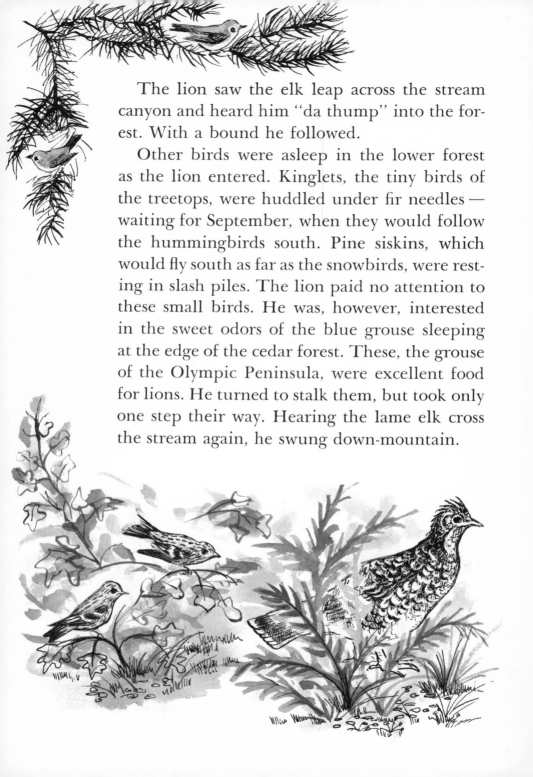

The lion saw the elk leap across the stream canyon and heard him "da thump" into the forest. With a bound he followed.

Other birds were asleep in the lower forest as the lion entered. Kinglets, the tiny birds of the treetops, were huddled under fir needles — waiting for September, when they would follow the hummingbirds south. Pine siskins, which would fly south as far as the snowbirds, were resting in slash piles. The lion paid no attention to these small birds. He was, however, interested in the sweet odors of the blue grouse sleeping at the edge of the cedar forest. These, the grouse of the Olympic Peninsula, were excellent food for lions. He turned to stalk them, but took only one step their way. Hearing the lame elk cross the stream again, he swung down-mountain.

He leaped the cascade and strode on. Some distance into the forest the lion stopped to check a new sound. A bull elk was moving in a glade on his right. He was alone, seeking out a quiet glen. This was his precourtship behavior. In September he would bugle like the monarch elk he was and call his harem to him. Now he was setting up his territory.

The lion swung his head. The sound of the "da thump" reached his sensitive ears. He could also hear the herd of elk and deer above him. It would take a month or more for them to work their way down. The injured elk, knowing the lion was after him, was going straight down the mountain in haste. The lion ran down the well-worn elk trail to the edge of another forest — the glorious rain forest, where the huge Sitka spruce, western hemlock, and Douglas fir grow to be two hundred and fifty feet high. The lion entered this gracious forest.

The limping elk was quiet. The lion paused at a spring to drink. Tiny frogs, which had just emerged from their tadpole stage and come onto the land, felt his step. They reacted by leaping back into the water. Rings from their dives knocked against the lion's nose. He lifted his head and curiously watched a frog climb ashore. It crept onto a bush and clung there by means of the suction pads on its feet. The lion turned his head and the frog plunged back into the spring.

The lion looked down. Beside his huge paw sat another amphibian — a northwestern hop toad. It too, had become an adult this month. Now, also frightened by the lion, the toad jumped, not into the spring like the frogs but into the woods. There the leaves and flowers would shelter it. The lion saw it bounce away like a rubber ball and followed it curiously. He nosed it as gently as a butterfly. The toad leaped four feet and disappeared.

The lion turned away, lifted his head, and smelled the elk. He slipped over the mossy rocks beside the spring and followed the stream it formed.

A struggle in the shallows caught his attention. He stopped. A large coho salmon fought his way, half out of water, toward a sandbar near the spring. On that bar he had hatched. Now, seven years later, he was trying to return to it — fighting, slashing his way back to the spot where he had started his life. With him moved a mate and other salmon intent upon their last mission — to reach the sandbar, spawn, and die.

The lion leaped downward. The moon was moving toward the east. A killdeer awoke beside the stream and called briefly. The bird fluttered, but the lion did not chase it. He was walking toward the top of a bluff where, far below, the stream met the Hoh River. The lion crouched. The limping elk was passing below. The young lion settled his feet squarely under him and tightened his muscles.

Suddenly he arose. His entire body focused on a moving object beyond the elk on the other side of the river. Among the skyscrapers of spruce, a shadow moved. It swayed in such harmony with the wind that only the night vision of a cat could distinguish it from the trees. The young lion felt what it was and a surge of warmth thumped through him. He forgot the elk and his hunger. The child lioness and her mother were swinging down the side of the river. Behind them strode the brother.

Still watching, the young lion lay down on his belly, placed his head on his paws, and studied the family as it took the narrow pass up the cliff toward the high meadows. He purred and rubbed his cheek on a paw.

He tensed and stood up. Coming down the same ledge was an enormous black bear. Head lowered, shoulder blades pumping up and down, the great bear of the north slope growled along.

At the bend the lioness and bear met. Both were surprised. Both reacted. The lioness swung her claw-rimmed paw and leaped, snarling, for the bear's neck. The bear reared, swung his powerful foot with its bladelike claws, and tore open the back of the lioness. He locked his teeth in her shoulder, and as he did, lost his footing. He began to fall, dragging the lioness with him. The riverbed lay forty feet below. Although they tore into the cliff with claws and paws, they could not stop their plunge. They fell free. Then there was silence. Presently the bear rolled to his feet and limped away. The lioness did not get up.

30

In rippling bounds the young lion came down
the bluff, crossed the Hoh, and stood beside the
lifeless cat. He howled.

A leaf, as large as a dinner plate and yellow
with the change of August, fell from the top of
the cliff. The big-leaf maple leaf spiraled to
the ground. The young lion looked up. Peer-
ing over the edge of the cliff was the child lioness. She cried. The young lion called to her.
Slowly she came down to meet him. He smelled
her ears and nose. He licked her cheek; then he
led her away from the riverbed. They walked
onto the territory that a moment ago had be-
longed to her mother.

The child lioness stayed close to the young
lion's heels. Far behind, moving cautiously,
came her yearling brother. The young lion
had a family. The orphans followed him as they
had followed their mother.

The three walked deep into the rain forest. Where the trees made columned hallways the child lioness took the lead. She led the young lion and her brother under vaulted spruce roots that were upholstered in soft club moss. They came into a glade where lacy ferns grew everywhere — on trees, rocks, limbs, other ferns. The floor around them was covered with oxalis — sour, bright grass that carpets the rain forest with three-leafed designs repeated everywhere.

The child lioness went on. She led the group to a moss-covered boulder. Leaping onto it with grace, she looked down upon the young lion. He vaulted to her side, watched her creep under an enormous log covered with ferns and air plants. She circled and lay down. Twigs and leaves beneath and around her marked the home of the mountain lions. The brother climbed the rock and lay down beside her.

Lowering himself to his belly, shoulders and haunches jutting, head erect, the young lion sat sphinxlike and stared at the child lioness.

It was almost dawn. The young lion dozed through that quiet time when the night animals are bedding down and the day animals are not yet up. Then the light came. The monkey flowers bobbed in the wind that stirs with the daybreak. The ferns took in dew, and some lost spores, or fern seeds, to the wind. The winter wren awoke and sang.

An exuberant little bird, this wren is a permanent resident of the rain forest. He does not migrate like the hummingbirds and swallows but stays in this fairyland all year. Now the wren sang only briefly, for it was August, and the singing and nesting seasons were over. The lion listened to the far-off drilling of a pileated woodpecker, a two-foot-high bird who matched the enormity of the rain forest. He sounded like distant thunder in the mossy dampness.

A chickaree scolded, announcing the passing of a bobcat, a cat about a third the size of the young lion. A raven sneaked through the trees on its way to the meadows to hunt mice. Then it was morning.

The three lions on the boulder still faced each other, paws tucked under their chests. Finally they closed their eyes and slept. Dull swishing sounds in the forest marked the homecoming of the black-tailed deer. They fed in the predawn and at twilight. They slept in bright daylight and during the dark night.

All day the lions slept, stretching and purring in the warmth of the August sun. This was the dry season and the sun shone all day — a rare event in this land where eight to ten feet of rain fell in the course of a year.

At sundown the mountain lions awoke. The child lioness leaped from the boulder and started down the family trail that led to the ocean. The young lion followed. Suddenly he leaped to the left. A flash of movement, a thud — and he felled a deer for his family. They dined, then proceeded toward the Pacific. Their trip was leisurely. They took two nights to go a few miles, for they ate and slept along the way.

Finally, when the moon was waning, the three lions came to the sea. From the edge of a sheer cliff they watched the waves roll in the moonlight.

Suddenly the young lion turned, and snarling, faced the female's brother. With a roar he fell upon him and knocked him down, then stood above him. The brother was subdued. Ears back, whiskers close against his face, he slunk into the forest. He never once looked back as he moved off to seek his own home far from here.

The young lion stood before the lioness. She purred, walked up to him, and rubbed her neck against his head. He purred. This sound grew into a mighty caterwaul that could not be muffled even by the ocean and the mossy trees. It terrified all that heard, except the lioness — the lion was in love.

39

Gathering all his strength, the young lion leaped down the cliff, vaulted over huge logs washed in by the sea, and sped lightly up the beach. The lioness ran close beside him. The moon of change was on the land. The young lion had a mate.

ABOUT THE AUTHOR

Jean Craighead George has been fascinated by the natural world all her life, and her books are based on her many experiences with the animals she writes about and on the countless books, articles, and scientific papers she reads. THE THIRTEEN MOONS has grown out of her special interest in ecology—particularly in phenology, the study of the relationship between climate and periodic biological events. As part of her research for THE MOON OF THE MOUNTAIN LIONS, Mrs. George climbed Mount Olympus in Washington and followed the trail taken down its slopes by the mountain lion in the book.

Mrs. George is co-author of DIPPER OF COPPER CREEK, which received the Aurianne Award for the most outstanding animal story published in 1957. MY SIDE OF THE MOUNTAIN, THE SUMMER OF THE FALCON, GULL NUMBER 737, SPRING COMES TO THE OCEAN, COYOTE IN MANHATTAN, and the books in the THE THIRTEEN MOONS series all have affirmed her remarkable sensitivity both to nature and to young people.

Mrs. George is a regular contributor of nature stories to *Reader's Digest*. She has held the position of art editor for *Pageant* magazine and served as a newspaper reporter for the *Washington Post* and International News Service.

ABOUT THE ILLUSTRATOR

"Drawing lions comes naturally for me," writes Winifred Lubell. "Our house pet is a Siamese-Burmese cat who looks and often acts like a mountain lion—but a very affectionate one, of course."

Mrs. Lubell is well known for the many children's books she has illustrated. A good number of these are filled with her special drawings of animals, insects, and birds. Some of the books were written by her husband.

For many years, Mrs. Lubell taught art to children. She now works as a hospital volunteer, teaching arts and crafts to disabled and underprivileged children in Westchester, where the Lubells live.